THOMAS TELFORD (1757–1834) was Britain's greatest civil engineer since the Romans, building roads, bridges, tunnels, canals, harbours and aqueducts. Every day thousands still drive along the A5 trunk road, which he surveyed and built from London to Holyhead nearly 150 years ago. He built the great bridges at Menai, Conway and Bettws-y-Coed. Among the many miles of canal he built were the Ellesmere Canal, the Caledonian Canal in Scotland and the Gotha Canal across Sweden. He built, designed, surveyed or advised on literally dozens of harbours from King's Lynn to Bude, from Plymouth to Wick and Tobermory.

Keith Ellis follows Telford's career which took this Scottish shepherd's son from Scotland to London, where he became an architect and then the most outstanding engineer of his time. This inspiring and very readable book contains a minimum of technical language, carefully used and backed up by a full glossary of terms. The book also contains more than fifty illustrations, a date chart, reading list and index.

KEITH ELLIS was born in 1927. He was educated at King Edward VII School, Sheffield, England, and gained an Open Exhibition to St. John's College, Cambridge University where he graduated in History. He has travelled widely in the U.S.A. and also in the Middle East, Malaysia, Australia and Canada. He has written many articles and several books, and is the author of *Thomas Edison and Telegraphy*, also in this series.

Thomas Telford

1757–1834

Father of Civil Engineering

Keith Ellis

Other Books in this Series

SBN 85078 186 8
Copyright © by Keith Ellis
First published in 1974 by
Wayland Publishers Limited
49 Lansdowne Place, Hove, East Sussex BN3 1HF
Second impression 1980
Printed and bound in Great Britain
at The Pitman Press, Bath

Contents

List of Illustrations

Introduction

"If you want to find his monument, look around." The inscription, in Latin, is carved over the north door of St. Paul's Cathedral in London and refers to the architect, Sir Christopher Wren. It could equally well apply to Thomas Telford (1757–1834). His work can still be seen in almost every part of Britain.

Every day, thousands drive along the A 5 trunk road, largely following the line he surveyed from London to Holyhead. Among the bridges he built are those at Menai, Conway, and Bettws-y-Coed. He built the Caledonian Canal and a network of roads and bridges in the Highlands of Scotland. He engineered the Carlisle to Glasgow Road.

The new town of Telford in Shropshire is named after him. He made his reputation as the county's surveyor and as engineer of the Ellesmere Canal. He was responsible for the building of Shrewsbury Gaol and the Church of St. Mary Magdalene, Bridgnorth.

He built, designed, surveyed or advised on literally dozens of harbours from King's Lynn to Bude, from Plymouth and Dover to Wick and Tobermory. He was consulted on a number of railways and reported on the drainage of the Fens.

If Telford is less well known today than Isambard Kingdom Brunel or Robert Stephenson, it is an accident of history. He rose to fame at the height of the canal-building era, making his name with the aqueducts that still soar majestically over the River Dee at Pont Cysyllte and over the River Ceiriog at Chirk. His Caledonian Canal remains one of the greatest achievements of civil engineering in the British Isles.

But the railway age was already dawning. Within half a century, a network of fast lines had captured the

The Menai Bridge as it is today. This takes the A5 across the Menai Straits from Caernarvonshire to Anglesey. Before 1825, which was when Telford's bridge was opened, communication between Anglesey and the mainland was kept up solely by ferry-boats.

bulk of freight traffic from the canals and had provided good passenger services. While millions experienced for themselves the convenience and excitement of travelling by rail, the canals fell into disuse. They attracted little freight. They became, literally, rural backwaters.

Telford's roads suffered a similar setback in public esteem. He himself saw them as busy highways, capable of carrying huge quantities of goods by fast steam carriages. Railway interests, however, kept steam carriages off the roads by pushing through Parliament restrictive legislation.

The roads did not come into their own until the invention of the internal combustion engine. Even then road haulage did not grow significantly until the 1930s. It was not until after the Second World War that Telford's roads became as busy as he had envisaged 150 years before. They were then quickly superseded by motorways.

Most of his works, then, though still in evidence, were overtaken by history. His main significance today is the part he played in making civil engineering a profession. He was not, of course, the first large-scale engineer, for James Brindley (1716–72) had already built the Grand Trunk Canal linking the Rivers Mersey and Trent. John Smeaton (1724–92) was responsible for the Forth and Clyde Canal, bridges at Perth, Banff and Coldstream, and a replacement for the second Eddystone Lighthouse. In Telford's own time, John Rennie (1761–1821) had engineered the Kennet and Avon Canal, London Bridge and Waterloo Bridge, and major harbour works at London, Plymouth, Hull, Sheerness, and Chatham.

Yet none had undertaken a scheme on anything like the scale of Telford's master plan for the Highlands of Scotland. That one man should be responsible for a scheme embracing more than a thousand bridges, 920 miles of new road, 42 churches and work on some two dozen harbours defies the imagination.

John Smeaton (1724–1792), one of the early canal-builders in Britain and the first Englishman to describe himself as a civil engineer. Among Smeaton's works was a replacement for the second Eddystone Lighthouse (pictured in the background).

He was able to do so only by using contractors on a scale never before known. Some of them employed up to a thousand men. Telford devised methods of supervising them which became standard practice.

His career culminated in his election as first President of the Institution of Civil Engineers. The choice was highly appropriate. By 1820, he was indisputably the head of his profession with an unprecendented quantity of work to his credit. But there was something else as well.

Civil engineering is a highly practical profession. Yet it also calls for great qualities of imagination. Telford combined both aspects. He had started his working life as a stone mason. Even when he had built the Caledonian Canal and the Menai Bridge, he was still proud to point out the gravestone he had inscribed in Langholm churchyard or the blocks he had hewn and laid while employed as a tradesman on the building of Somerset House.

From masonry, he had graduated to architecture, a profession he followed until the age of thirty-eight. He spent much of his free time studying and drawing buildings which appealed to him. Add to this the qualities of imagination that gave him an appreciation of landscape and the ability to write poetry good enough for publication and we see why much of his engineering work achieved a rare grandeur.

As a character, Telford is hard to pin down. He was undoubtedly attractive with a laughing, lop-sided face and strong curly hair. He had an easy manner which enabled him to get on with every class of man. He was as much at home with poets, professors, land-owners, and parliamentarians as with his beloved "navvy boys" with whom he regularly ate on equal terms, each paying for his own dinner.

Yet he could be ruthless with any who failed to measure up to his standards, as poor John Duncombe found (chapter 4). Though fond of children and young people, he never married and we never hear of his making a close relationship with a woman, least of all with the mother from whom he was so often separated during his childhood.

There seems little doubt that his unremitting application to work was in some measure a compen-

A middle-aged Thomas Telford—still with the strong curly hair that he had as a young lad.

sation for the lack of a normal home life. If he had married as a jobbing mason, it is hard to imagine that he could have made the moves and taken the risks on which his career was built. He would have been too busy working to keep his family.

Whether he lost or gained is a matter of opinion. He was never a money-grubber and undertook vast projects for derisory fees. Often he worked for nothing. He enjoyed his work immensely and kept his enthusiasm to the very end. The story of his life is a saga of energy and achievement rarely surpassed in British history.

Telford's birthplace, by the Megget Water near Westerkirk, Dumfriesshire. Now, just over two hundred years later, all that remains of this shepherd's croft is a few stones.

1 *The Young Mason*

The man who revolutionized civil engineering and became Britain's greatest road and bridge builder since the Romans was born the son of a shepherd a few miles north of Langholm in Dumfriesshire.

The family home was a mud house with a thatched roof built on a mound by the Megget, a burn which joins the River Esk at the nearby hamlet of Westerkirk to the south. All around rose the green hills of the Glendinning farm on which John Telford tended sheep. It was remote and peaceful. Yet until the Act of Union was signed between England and Scotland half a century before, it had been the scene of bloody border raids.

Thomas Telford himself was born on 9th August 1757. Three months later, John Telford died and his widow, Janet, had to find a new home for herself and her only son. The following Whitsuntide, they took one room of a two-roomed cottage at The Crooks, halfway between Glendinning and Westerkirk.

The "Crooks," where Janet, Thomas's mother, moved with her young son, six months after her husband's death.

They had no money and Mrs. Telford took jobs on neighbouring farms. She milked, sheared and helped with haymaking. Often her young son was left with friends.

Soon, he himself was working. In summer, he lived with a relative employed as a shepherd. In winter, he stayed at neighbouring farms. In return for his board, lodging and five shillings a year for clogs, he ran errands and did odd jobs. Luckily, another relative was able to pay the small fee enabling him to attend Westerkirk parish school, where he learned the three "Rs."

It scarcely seems a promising start in life. If we look more closely, however, we see that it provided a firm foundation for his particular talents. The long hours spent on the hills looking after sheep gave him a liking for the lonely places in which so much of his later work had to be done. He got a feeling for landscape and came to know almost by instinct the easiest and most pleasing course for a road or canal.

His constant change of home and separation from his mother made it hard for him to form deep relationships with other people, especially women. But he learned how to get on with almost everybody. He was well liked by his school-fellows, mostly the sons of farmers and small landowners. His education, though elementary by our standards, was sound enough to enable him to teach himself whatever he needed to know. "I still recollect with pride and pleasure my native parish of Westerkirk," he wrote in old age.

When he left school, probably at fourteen, there were only two careers open to him. He could become a farm-worker or an artisan. It was decided to apprentice him to a stone mason in Lochmaben, a small town between Lockerbie and Dumfries, but he was so badly treated that after a few months he ran away. Luckily, his mother's cousin, Thomas Jackson, was land steward to Sir James Johnstone of nearby Wester

Westerkirk Church and School.

16

Hall. Jackson was able to arrange for Telford to continue his apprenticeship under Andrew Thomson, a mason in Langholm.

There was no shortage of work. The local landowner, the Duke of Buccleuch, was busily improving local roads and his tenants' houses. Bridges were required to carry wheeled carriages over streams. Telford progressed from an apprentice to a journeyman. He now lived in Langholm and returned to The Crooks only at weekends.

His thick curly hair, ruddy features and easy manner soon made "Laughing Tammy" a popular figure. He was invited to call on Miss Pasley, an elderly spinster who lived in one of Langholm's few substantial houses. She offered him the run of her small library. Reading *Paradise Lost* on a hillside was a revelation. "I read, and read, and glowred," he wrote later, "then read, and read again." Burns was another favourite. Soon, he himself was writing highly competent verse, some of which was published.

He was now earning one shilling and sixpence a day. He worked on a number of new houses going up in the town, on Westerkirk manse and on the Esk bridge, where his mason's mark can still be seen.

Soon after the bridge had been built, heavy rain turned the river into a torrent. The master mason was away from home and his wife was sure the bridge would be swept away. As her husband had agreed to keep it in good repair for seven years, this would have meant financial disaster. In a panic, she told Telford, "They say it's shakin'." He reassured her, "I like it a' the better that it shakes—it proves it's well put thegither." She refused to be comforted and braced herself against the parapet in an effort to hold the bridge together. Telford simply stood and laughed.

Work grew less plentiful. For a while, he carved ornamental doorheads and gravestones, including one for the father he had never known. He inscribed it: "In memory of John Telford, who after living 33 years

Telford's mason's mark.

an unblameable shepherd, died at Glendinning, November, 1757." He then moved to Edinburgh.

The next two years were crucial. He earned good money working on the New Town which was then being built. More important, he found craftsmanship of a standard undreamed of at Langholm. He became interested in architecture and spent hours wandering round Edinburgh with a sketching-pad. He studied the Castle, Holyrood House and Heriot's Hospital. He visited the old chapel of Rosslyn and Melrose Abbey.

He now realized that he would never be satisfied with the limited opportunities available in Scotland and decided to seek his fortune in London. On a

Edinburgh Castle was one of the buildings in Edinburgh which Telford studied and which inspired him to become an architect himself.

S.E. VIEW of EDINBURGH CASTLE.

19

farewell visit to Langholm, he made the rounds of his old friends. Then came a stroke of luck. His cousin, Thomas Jackson, heard that Sir James Johnstone had promised a horse to a member of his family living in London. He was looking for some means of getting it there. Jackson suggested that Telford should ride it.

A few days later, wearing his cousin's buckskin breeches, Telford set out on horseback. "Having acquired," he wrote later, "the rudiments of my profession, I considered that my native country afforded few opportunities of exercising it to any extent and therefore judged it advisable (like many of my countrymen) to proceed southward, where industry might find more employment and be better remunerated."

Heriot's Hospital was another of the magnificent buildings in Edinburgh that Telford visited and sketched.

20

2 *From Mason to Architect*

Telford arrived in London with two valuable assets. One was a letter of introduction from Miss Pasley of Eskdale to her brother Mr. John Pasley, an eminent London merchant. The other was his link with the Johnstone family.

John Pasley gave him two further letters of introduction. The first was to Robert Adam, the distinguished architect, who was friendly but could not help him. The other was to Sir William Chambers, an equally distinguished architect, who was cold and remote but gave him a job as a mason on Somerset

This was the Edinburgh that Telford saw in 1780, with a population of about forty thousand. The New Town, which Telford worked on was being built between the far side of the Old Town and the river. Over the following ten years the population of Edinburgh almost doubled.

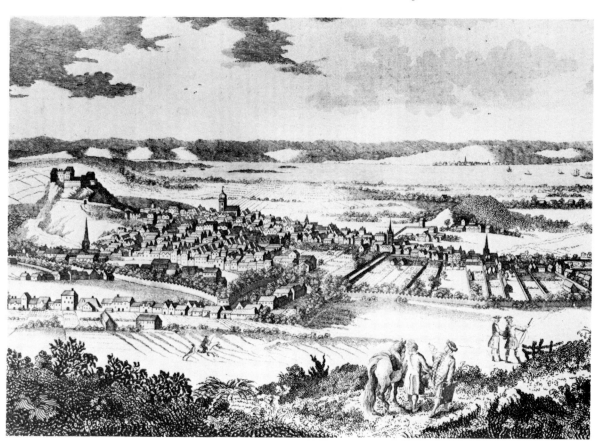

Sir William Chambers (1726–1796), one of the greatest architects in London, and the first man to give Telford work there.

House which Chambers was then building.

Telford was well paid but he saw little future in working as a mason. His colleagues spent their week's earnings before the end of the following week. If he was to make real progress, he must strike out on his own. He tried to form a partnership with a Mr. Hatton who had "extraordinary skill and abilities." Between them, he claimed, "there is nothing done in stone or marble that we cannot do in the completest manner." But though Robert Adam promised his support, the partnership foundered on the rock that has sunk so many building firms before and since—shortage of capital.

Luckily, Telford had another string to his bow. Sir James Johnstone's son, William, had married Miss Pulteney, niece of the Earl of Bath. She brought him a

Telford was set to work by Chambers on the New Public Offices at Somerset House *above*. He worked well and was quickly promoted. Whenever, in later life, he crossed Waterloo Bridge, he would proudly point out to his friends the stones which he had laid in the south-west corner of the building.

large fortune and he took her family name. When he succeeded to his father's baronetcy in 1797, he became Sir William Pulteney and represented first Cromarty, then Shrewsbury, in seven successive parliaments. His business acumen made him the wealthiest commoner in the country. He had more pocket boroughs in his gift than anyone else.

Pulteney became Telford's patron. While still a mason at Somerset House, Telford advised on alterations that Pulteney was planning at Wester Hall.

What happened next is not clear. But after two years in London, he was given the job of supervising the building of a house for the Commissioner of Portsmouth Dockyard. It had been designed by the architect Samuel Wyatt. Telford was no longer a journeyman mason but a foreman.

He was already preparing for his next step. While making sure that the job in hand was done so well "that none shall be able to eclipse me," he wrote poetry, joined the Freemasons, had his hair powdered every day and put on a clean shirt three times a week. Gentlemen now treated the shepherd's son as an equal.

Yet most of his leisure was spent in private study. He examined in detail the construction of wharves and graving docks. He set himself a programme of reading that went far beyond the needs of the moment and qualified him for the more difficult jobs ahead. He told a friend in a letter how he spent his days:

"I rise in the morning at 7 (February 1) and will get up earlier as the days lengthen until it comes to 5 o'clock. I immediately set to work to make out accounts, write on matters of business, or draw, until breakfast, which is at 9. Then I go into the Yard about 10, see that all are at their posts, and am ready to advise about any matters that may require attention. This, and going round the several works, occupies until about dinner-time, which is at 2; and after that I again go round and attend to what may be wanted. I draw till 5; then tea; and after that I write, draw or read until half after 9; and then comes supper and bed. This is my ordinary round, unless I dine or spend an evening with a friend; but I do not make many friends, being very particular, nay, nice to a degree. My business requires a good deal of writing and drawing, and this work I always take care to keep under by reserving my time for it, and being in advance of my work rather than behind it. Then, as knowledge is my most ardent pursuit, a thousand things occur which call for investigation which would pass unnoticed by those who are content to trudge only in the beaten path. I am not contented unless I can give a reason for every particular method or practice which is pursued. Hence, I am now very deep in chemistry. The

The Church of St. Mary Magdalene at Bridgnorth, Shropshire, which Telford designed in 1788.

mode of making mortar in the best way led me to inquire into the nature of lime. Having, in pursuit of this inquiry, looked into some books on chemistry, I perceived the field was boundless; but that to assign satisfactory reasons for many mechanical processes required a general knowledge of that science. I have therefore borrowed a manuscript copy of Dr. Black's Lectures. I have bought his 'Experiments on Magnesia and Quicklime' and also Fourcroy's Lectures, translated from the French by one Mr. Elliot, of Edinburgh. And I am determined to study the subject with unwearied attention until I attain some accurate knowledge of chemistry, which is of less use in the practice of the arts than it is in that of medicine."

Pulteney kept a close eye on Telford's progress. He had large estates in Shrewsbury and as soon as the Portsmouth job was finished, hired Telford to supervise alterations to his own residence, Shrewsbury Castle. Shortly afterwards, probably through Pulteney's influence, Telford was appointed county surveyor. He was just thirty.

It was the surveyor's job to advise the magistrates on the maintenance of roads, bridges, and public buildings under their control. He then carried out their orders. By the summer of 1788, Telford was working on ten separate jobs including drainage works and a new hospital and jail in Shrewsbury. But he still found time to do outside work. He excavated the Roman city of Uriconium and designed the church of St. Mary Magdalene in Bridgnorth.

Today, the post of county surveyor is nearly always filled by a civil engineer. At this time, the profession barely existed. Telford concentrated on architecture. He still made careful notes of his study of chemistry, mechanics, pneumatics, and hydrostatics which were all important to a builder. He also copied out long

extracts from the leading architectural works of the time. In 1792, he made a study tour of Gloucester, Worcester, Bath, Oxford, and London. He examined the main public buildings. He worked in the libraries of the British Museum and of the Antiquarian Society.

Yet his job demanded what we should now call civil engineering. He had already designed and built one bridge over the River Severn near the village of Montford. In 1795, heavy rainfall turned the Severn into a raging flood. It destroyed the bridge at Buildwas and seriously damaged those at Bewdley and Bridgnorth.

These were just three of the forty road bridges for which he was responsible between 1790 and 1796. They were important because they made his local reputation as an engineer. His new bridge at Buildwas was made of iron, then a novel material in bridge-building, pioneered in the famous bridge at Coalbrookdale. He was attracted to it because it made possible a single span which would not get in the way of boats and was less likely to be swept away when the river was in spate. He improved on the hundred-foot Coalbrookdale bridge by flattening the arch. He also made it lighter by half, even though it was thirty feet longer. This reduced the weight on the foundations.

He was capable and well liked. Jolly and sociable, he was able to get on with everyone from his patron, Pulteney, to the workmen who hewed the stone. He read widely, wrote poetry and visited the theatre whenever a company played in Shrewsbury. Yet he was abstemious, too, drinking only water and avoiding sweets. His usual supper was boiled oatmeal with milk.

Local landowners and businessmen had already marked him as an up-and-coming man. As early as 1793, they begged him to become "general agent" of the newly formed Ellesmere Canal Company. The idea was to link the Rivers Mersey, Dee, and Severn, a far greater undertaking than any he had yet tackled.

The famous Coalbrookdale bridge, the first iron bridge in England, was designed by an almost unknown architect—Thomas Farnolls Pritchard—and completed in 1777 after his death by Daniel Onions. The bridge sections were cast by Abraham Darby, the pioneer of coke smelting, in his Coalbrookdale Foundry nearby.

Telford's iron bridge across the Severn at Buildwas, built in 1795 after floods had destroyed the earlier stone bridge there. Telford's use of iron was inspired by the Coalbrookdale Iron Bridge *above*.

Despite his ambition, Telford had not even applied
for the job because he thought it was beyond his
powers. When it was offered, he accepted gladly. It
was "the greatest work now in hand in this kingdom."
It was to give him a national reputation every bit as
glowing as the one he had already enjoyed in
Shropshire.

Telford's 1798 bridge across the
Severn at Bewdley.

3 *The Ellesmere Canal*

Why was the post of general agent to a canal company in one of England's remotest counties so important?

We must remember that this was the great age of inland waterways. At the time of Telford's appointment, "canal mania" was sweeping the country. Railways had not yet appeared. Most roads were so poor that in winter only packhorses could struggle through the all-engulfing mud.

Canals offered the only year-round means of transport. The companies that owned them did not themselves carry goods. They charged tolls on the goods carried by other people.

The first canal had been built in 1763 by James Brindley. It was a short stretch from the Duke of Bridgewater's colliery at Worsley into Manchester. By

A standard cast-iron road bridge built by Telford over a tributary of the Severn at Atcham, Shropshire. It has been preserved and discreetly strengthened for modern traffic by encasing the inner sections in concrete.

MᴿJAMES BRINDLEY.

cutting transport costs, it brought down the price of coal in Manchester. Yet local businessmen were not convinced. When the Duke drove a second canal from Manchester to Runcorn and Liverpool, he had to find the money in London.

The Manchester–Liverpool Canal was a huge success. Suddenly, everyone wanted to cash in on the advantages offered by canals. Industrialists saw them as a means of bringing raw materials to their factories and of carrying the finished products all over

Left James Brindley (1716–1772), the "father" of canal-building in Britain had dreamed of joining the four great rivers, Mersey, Humber, Severn and Thames by a system of canals. He got as far as surveying and planning the routes for the whole of the system, but died before it could be completed.

The first of Brindley's canals was the Bridgewater Canal built over a difficult course from Worsley to Manchester. The aqueduct at Barton shown *above* took this canal across the River Inwell, a tributary of the River Mersey.

England, and also to the ports for export. The canals brought lime, manure, and roofing slate to farmers. They gave easy access to city markets. Rents of remote farms rose. Landowners, industrialists, and farmers all clamoured for canals and the people who put up the money to build them usually made good profits.

Brindley, who died in 1772, had always dreamed of a canal "cross," a system of waterways linking the Mersey, Humber, Severn, and Thames. He completed the first arm with his Grand Trunk Canal from the

Mersey to the Trent. By January 1790, the cross was completed when the Oxford Canal finally linked this with the Thames. A connection with the Severn already existed. Canal promoters were now busily filling in the gaps between the arms.

Shropshire's collieries and ironworks were as yet badly served. The River Severn was navigable all the way to Welshpool in Montgomeryshire, but floods and droughts often made the upper reaches impassable. The only canals were a few short channels linking the collieries and ironworks around Ketley to the Severn at Coalport.

The Ellesmere Canal Company planned a waterway linking the Severn at Shrewsbury with the River Dee at Chester and with the Mersey at what is now Ellesmere Port. Their task was formidable. If they chose a route east of the Dee, the canal would be too far from the industrial centres of Wrexham and Ruabon. If they followed a line west of the Dee, they would have to build through appallingly difficult country.

The company appointed William Jessop of Newark as its engineer. He was what we should now call a consultant. Two local men, John Duncombe and William Turner, made surveys of the two routes and the company accepted Jessop's recommendation of the western one.

At this point, Telford was asked to attend a general meeting of the shareholders. He faced a delicate situation. Some still thought an eastern route preferable. Others felt that the job as general agent should go to Turner. So did Jessop. But John Wilkinson, "king of the iron-masters," pushed through Telford's appointment.

His official title was "general agent, surveyor, engineer, architect, and overlooker of the canal." His brief covered "all architectural and engineering business . . . the drawing, forming, and directing the making of bridges, aqueducts, tunnels, locks, buildings, reservoirs, wharfs, and other works." He

A plan of the Ellesmere Canal published in 1795 when the first stretch—between Chester and Ellesmere Port—was opened.

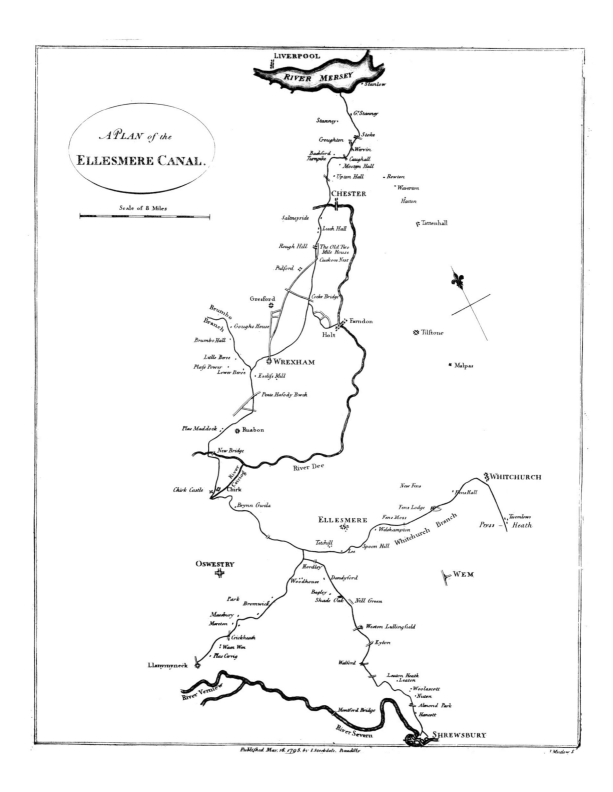

A PLAN of the ELLESMERE CANAL.

Scale of 8 Miles

LIVERPOOL

RIVER MERSEY

Stanlow

G.ᵗ Stanney

Stanney

Stoke

Croughton

Wervin

Backford
Turnpike

Caughall

Moston Hall

Upton Hall

Rowton

Waverton

Hatton

CHESTER

Tattenhall

Saltneyside

Leech Hall

Rough Hill

The Old Two
Mile House

Pulford

Cuckoos Nest

Gresford

Cocks Bridge

Farndon

Brumbo
Branch

Goughs House

Holt

Tilstone

Brumbo Hall

Malpas

Lulle Borse

Plass Power

Lower Borse

Eveliss Mill

WREXHAM

Penu Hafody Bwch

Plas Maddock

Ruabon

New Bridge

River Ceiriog

River Dee

WHITCHURCH

New Fens

Fens Hall

Chirk Castle

Chirk

Fens Lodge

Twemlows
Heath

Brynn Gwila

ELLESMERE

Fens Moss

Press - Heath

Welshampton

Whitchurch Branch

Tetchill

Spoon Hill

Lee

OSWESTRY

WEM

Hordley

Woodhouse

Dandyford

Bagley

Nill Green

Park

Bromwick

Shads Oak

Maesbury

Weston Lullingfield

Moreton

Crickheath

Eyton

Waen Wen

Plas Cerrig

Walford

Llanymyneck

Leaton Heath

Leaton

Woolascott

Nuten

River Verniew

Almond Park

Hancott

Montford Bridge

River Severn

SHREWSBURY

Published Mar. 16. 1795. by I. Stockdale, Piccadilly

I. Mutlow S.

was "to superintend the cutting, forming, and making of the Canal . . . to give instructions for contracts, to attend himself (or some confidential person by him employed) to the execution of all the contracts . . . to pay contractors and workmen and to keep accounts."

His salary was to be £500 a year out of which he had to pay a clerk, a confidential foreman and his own journey expenses. Later, it was dropped to £300 and his assistants placed on the company payroll. Despite this new load of work, he remained county surveyor of Shropshire until he died. However, he was now in a position to turn down small private jobs "which give a great deal of very unpleasant labour for very little profit; in short they are like the calls of a country surgeon."

Telford now needed all his skill in working amicably with others. Both Turner and Duncombe were his subordinates and Turner clearly resented it. Moreover, Telford was required to submit all drawings to Jessop for his consideration and correction. However, both were expert in their own fields—Telford in masonry, Jessop in canal cutting. Each recognized the other's skill and a good relationship quickly emerged.

The first stretch of canal was straightforward. It ran across the flat Wirral peninsula between Chester and Ellesmere Port. It could take boats up to fourteen feet wide and from its opening in 1795 attracted a heavy volume of freight. Two passenger boats connected with the Liverpool ferry at Ellesmere Port. The service was so popular that a concessionaire paid £1,000 a year for hiring them, together with the Ellesmere Canal Tavern.

At the same time, work was going forward on a branch from the main line about six miles east of Oswestry to link with the Montgomeryshire Canal which ran to Welshpool and Newtown. The section of the main line from Chester to Ruabon was, however, postponed. In fact it was never built. There remained

The Pont Cysyllte aqueduct carrying the Ellesmere Canal 127 feet above the Dee valley. Work on the aqueduct started in July 1795 and took almost ten years to complete.

the final section of the main line which meant crossing the Dee and Ceiriog valleys. Telford now turned his main attention to this.

The Dee crossing at Pont Cysyllte was a challenge of the greatest magnitude. The valley was nearly 350 yards across and the river flowed 127 feet below the line of the canal on each side. James Brindley had carried his canals across smaller valleys on aqueducts. The water lay in a stone channel lined with clay. The weight was enormous. To support it, the piers had to be short and thick. "After all this expense," wrote Telford, "the frosts, by swelling the moist puddle [clay], frequently created fissures, which burst the masonry and suffered the water to escape—nay, sometimes actually threw down the aqueduct."

He was far from happy when the company approved plans, prepared by Turner, for a similar structure at Pont Cysyllte. They called for a series of locks at each side of the crossing to bring the level of the canal down to a low, three-arch aqueduct. Telford got the plans stopped, whereupon Turner resigned.

Telford's own suggestion for tackling the problem was revolutionary. He wanted to carry the canal straight across in a light, cast iron trough supported by tall, slender piers. Luckily, he was able to try out the method on a smaller scale first. He had just been appointed engineer to the Shrewsbury Canal, which was to link the Ketley canal with Shrewsbury. He demonstrated the feasibility of a cast iron trough with a single-span aqueduct over the River Tern near Longdon. This helped to convince doubters who could not envisage a canal carrying boats 127 feet above the Dee valley.

The Pont Cysyllte aqueduct had nineteen 53-foot spans. The piers were only nine feet by twelve feet at the top. To save weight, they were built solid for only the first 70 feet, the rest being hollow with two-foot thick outer walls and cross walls inside. The cast iron trough was eleven feet ten inches wide. Iron pillars in its bed carried a tow-path of four feet eight inches, leaving a width of seven feet two inches for boats.

Work started on 25th July, 1795. Telford's foreman on the job was Matthew Davidson, who had been a fellow mason at Langholm many years before. At Telford's invitation, Davidson had first worked for Pulteney at Bath, then on Montford Bridge (see chapter 2), where John Simpson, a Shrewsbury mason, was also employed. Now, Davidson and his young family were installed in a cottage by the aqueduct. James Varley of Colne, Lancashire, had originally contracted to build the piers but the job proved too big for him. Telford brought in John Simpson to support him. Later, Simpson, with his assistant John Wilson, of Dalston, Cumberland, took over the entire contract. Davidson, Simpson, and Wilson spent the rest of their lives working for Telford. William Hazledine, a fellow Freemason who

Telford's Chirk aqueduct on the Ellesmere Canal, built between 1796 and 1801.

supplied the ironwork, also cooperated with Telford on many later projects.

Meanwhile, Telford was responsible for building the rest of the canal. At the south end of the Pont Cysyllte aqueduct, he provided an approach embankment almost a hundred feet high. It was the biggest yet built in England. Further south, the canal passed through two tunnels, each of which was unusual in having a towpath. This saved bargees the chore of pushing their boats along by thrusting against the tunnel sides with their feet.

Then came the Chirk aqueduct which carried the canal seventy feet above the River Ceiriog with ten forty-foot arches. The piers were similar to those at Pont Cysyllte. Above the arches, two walls ran the full length of the aqueduct. Telford wrote:

"Across these, the canal bottom was formed by cast iron plates at each side, infixed in square stone masonry. These bottom plates had flanges on their edges, and were secured by nuts and screws at every juncture. The sides of the canal were made waterproof by ashlar masonry, backed with hard burnt bricks laid in Parker's cement, on the outside of which was rubble stone work.

"The towing path had a thin bed of clay under the gravel, and its outer edge was protected by an iron railing. The width of the waterway is 11 feet; of the masonry on each side, 5 feet 6 inches; and the depth of the water in the canal 5 feet. By this mode of construction the quantity of masonry is much diminished, and the iron bottom plate forms a continuous tie, preventing the side-walls from separation by lateral pressure of the contained water."

Despite these superb feats of engineering, the scheme as a whole was not going smoothly. When it was decided that the central section was too difficult to build, a tramway was built to link the canal with the collieries and ironworks near Ruabon. But the

Wrexham traffic was lost for ever.

Moreover, the canal had no water supply. Every time a boat passed through a lock, a lockful of water was lost downstream. Unless it was replaced, the level of the upper reaches would fall until they were no longer navigable. Telford overcame the difficulty by driving a "feeder" canal through the Vale of Llangollen to Llantisilio. Here, he built the Horseshoe Falls to draw water from the River Dee. He then made an arrangement with Sir Watkin Williams Wynn, a local landowner, to maintain a high level of water in Lake Bala by means of a weir. The Dee ran down from Lake Bala. If its level should fall, water could be released from the lake. The water level of the canal was thus protected against every contingency.

Yet in a sense, the canal was still high and dry. The company had run out of money. They were unable to continue to Shrewsbury and the southern section of the main line came to an end at Weston Lullingfields. It was thus isolated from both the Severn and the Mersey, the two important rivers it had been meant to connect.

There was only one solution. Some years before, the Chester Canal had been built from Chester to Nantwich. Originally, the owners had planned a branch to the Trent and Mersey Canal at Middlewich. However, the owners of the Trent and Mersey thought that they would lose traffic if this happened. So they arranged for an extra clause to be inserted in the Act of Parliament which gave the Chester Canal people permission to build. It stated that the Middlewich branch must not come closer than fifty yards to the line of the Trent and Mersey. Clearly, there was no point in building the branch under these conditions. The Chester Canal was almost ruined.

Now, however, a way was found to rescue both the Chester and the Ellesmere Canals. The Ellesmere had originally planned a branch to Whitchurch and on this work was going well. It was now decided to ex-

Map of England showing the canals with which Telford was connected.

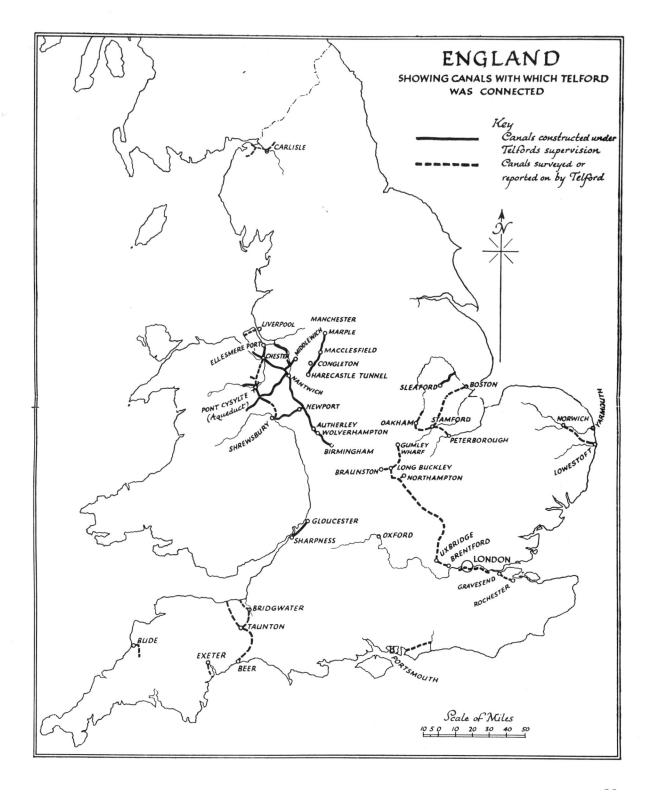

ENGLAND

SHOWING CANALS WITH WHICH TELFORD WAS CONNECTED

Key
Canals constructed under
Telfords supervision
Canals surveyed or
reported on by Telford

N

CARLISLE

LIVERPOOL
MANCHESTER
MARPLE
ELLESMERE PORT
MIDDLEWICH
MACCLESFIELD
CHESTER
CONGLETON
HARECASTLE TUNNEL
NANTWICH
SLEAFORD
BOSTON
PONT CYSYLTE
(Aqueduct)
NEWPORT
OAKHAM
STAMFORD
NORWICH
YARMOUTH
SHREWSBURY
AUTHERLEY
WOLVERHAMPTON
PETERBOROUGH
LOWESTOFT
BIRMINGHAM
GUMLEY
WHARF
BRAUNSTON
LONG BUCKLEY
NORTHAMPTON
GLOUCESTER
OXFORD
SHARPNESS
UXBRIDGE
BRENTFORD
LONDON
GRAVESEND
ROCHESTER
BRIDGWATER
TAUNTON
BUDE
EXETER
BEER
PORTSMOUTH

Scale of Miles
10 5 0   10   20   30   40   50

39

tend it to Hurleston, a few miles north of Nantwich. Here it joined the Chester Canal. By 1805, therefore, it was possible to sail from Pont Cysyllte to the Mersey, but only by taking a looping detour through Whitchurch and Hurlestone.

The Pont Cysyllte aqueduct was opened to traffic in the same year. It had become one of the wonders of Wales and, even while it was being built, visitors came from all parts to see the work in progress. Sir Walter Scott called it "the most impressive work of art he had ever seen," On 26th November, 1805, a crowd of 8,000 sang "God Save the King" and "Rule Britannia" as the first six boats sailed in line ahead 127 feet up in the sky. The Royal Artillery Company fired a royal salute.

Telford's reputation was now made. He had been mason, architect, and county surveyor. Now he was universally acknowledged as one of Britain's leading civil engineers. His work on the Ellesmere Canal was largely finished. He resigned as general agent, though he was retained as consultant until 1828.

4 *Master Plan for the Highlands*

Telford was now forty-eight. As a man, he seemed to have changed very little since his days as a mason. He was extremely sociable, though all his deeper friendships were with men, never women. He read widely, continued to write poetry, enjoyed studying architecture and shared the romantic feelings of his contemporaries for the landscape. His only blind spot was music. "The melody of sound is thrown away upon me," he said. "It must be a defect; but it is a fact and I cannot help it."

He still kept in touch with his old friends in Eskdale. Much of what we know about his daily life comes from the letters he wrote to Andrew Little, a former school-fellow who lost his sight while serving as a surgeon in Africa and became a teacher in Langholm. He regularly sent Little money to be spent on small comforts for his (Telford's) mother. She had said that she did not want money from her son and Little had to be sure that she never found out who was helping her.

In 1794, Telford visited her for the last time. His feelings were mixed. "Indeed, I am rather distressed at the thoughts of running down to see a kind parent in the last stage of decay," he wrote. "I can only bestow on her an affectionate look and then leave her. Her mind will not be much consoled by this parting, and the impression left upon mine will be more lasting than pleasant."

He saw all his old friends in Langholm. They found him as affable as ever and "not a bit set up." Frank Beattie, a former mason, was now an inn-keeper and confessed he had lost his tools. "I have taken better care of mine," said Telford. "I have them all locked up in a room at Shrewsbury, as well as my old working

The Pont Cysyllte aqueduct on the Ellesmere Canal, opened on 26th November, 1805.

clothes and leather apron: you know one can never tell what may happen."

We have seen how he became general agent of the Ellesmere Canal Company while still county surveyor of Shropshire. As his reputation grew, requests for his services came from all sides. While attending to the building of bridges, tunnels, and aqueducts, he found time to advise on water works for Liverpool and Glasgow. He helped improve the navigation of the River Severn and submitted plans for a new, single-span, iron London Bridge, which was never built. He quickly came to know a great many politicians, industrialists, academics, civil engineers, and what we should now call civil servants.

He described his life at this time in another letter to Little. "A few days since, I attended a general assembly of the canal proprietors in Shropshire. I have to be at Chester again in a week, upon an arbitration business respecting the rebuilding of the county hall and gaol; but previous to that, I must visit Liverpool, and afterwards proceed into Worcestershire. It is something like Buonaparte, when in Italy, fighting battles at fifty or a hundred miles distance every other day. However, plenty of employment is what every professional man is seeking . . ."

In the middle of all this activity, he started on his most important work. In 1796, his old patron, Pulteney, asked him to advise on the use of Parker's cement, which was waterproof. Would it be suitable for the underwater footings of port buildings? It seemed a trivial request. Yet the consequences were

Telford's plans for a cast-iron London Bridge were put forward in 1801, but the bridge, pictured above, was never built.

Throughout the Highlands, conditions were primitive and life was hard. This picture shows the inside of a poor weaver's cottage on the island of Islay in 1774. One of the many churches later built by Telford in some of the remotest places in the Highlands is to be found on the same island.

great, for Pulteney was governor of the British Fisheries Society, a joint stock company whose aim was to revive the Highlands fishing industry. Telford became the Society's engineer.

At this time, the Highlands were a waste created by the Duke of Cumberland who defeated the Young Pretender at Culloden in 1746 and became known as "The Butcher" for his subsequent cruelties. The Clans were broken up, their lands confiscated. Though they were restored to the chiefs in 1787, they were mostly turned over to sheep.

Conditions were primitive in the extreme. In many districts, good timber was plentiful. The Highlanders sold only the bark, leaving the trees to rot in the ground. They had no ploughs. Instead, they used a crude tool called the cas-chrom which they pushed and turned by hand. They were chronically short of food. In many districts, the only grain cultivated was barley and oats for cattle.

An Argyllshire minister wrote of his parishioners: "They were obliged to bleed their cattle, in order to subsist some time on their blood (boiled); and even the inhabitants of the glens and valleys repaired in crowds to the shore, at the distance of three or four miles, to pick up the scanty provision which the shell-fish afforded them."

Sick of starving by their turf fires, thousands emigrated. It seemed only a matter of time before the Highlands were totally deserted.

The British Fisheries Society tried to help matters by building fishing ports at Tobermory and Ullapool. They soon realized that they were only tinkering with the problem. What the Highlands most needed was roads.

The only roads then existing were those built by the English general George Wade between 1726 and 1740 to enable his troops to move quickly against future rebels. There were 800 miles of these "military roads." One followed the line of the Great Glen across the centre of Inverness-shire and was joined by another that ran through Glencoe and Tyndrum and along the western bank of Loch Lomond to the Lowlands. A third ran from Fort Augustus in the Great Glen to Blair Atholl and Dunkeld. A fourth linked Fort George with Badenoch, Braemar, and Coupar Angus.

The Highlanders found Wade's roads of little use. Instead, they took to cattle tracks through the mountains. Heavy goods and wheeled vehicles were shut out of large areas. The journey from Edinburgh to

Map of Scotland showing General George Wade's military roads and th roads later built by Telford.

Inverness (now 158 miles) took eight days. And it was dangerous. "There was no bridge over the Tay at Dunkeld," wrote Lord Henry Cockburn, the famous Scottish judge, "or over the Spey at Fochabers, or over the Findhorn at Forres. Nothing but wretched pierless ferries, let to poor cottars, who rowed or hauled, or pushed a crazy boat across, or more commonly got their wives to do it." There were long delays when ferries broke down or were held up by floods. Accidents were frequent and many travellers were drowned.

Beyond Inverness, communications were even worse. There were no bridges over the Rivers Beauly or Conon and drovers had to swim across with their cattle. Wheeled carts were almost unknown in Caithness. The interior of Sutherland was almost inaccessible. The only "road" was a coastal track which was covered by the tide for part of each day. Goods were carried to and from this track by packhorse or on the backs of women.

Alarmed by the continuing flight from the Highlands, the government finally decided to act. On 27th July, 1801, Nicholas Vansittart, Joint Secretary to the Treasury asked Telford to report on communications generally but with particular reference to ports and possible stations for fisheries. Naval requirements and links with Ireland and Europe were also to be taken into consideration.

Telford was away almost four months. We do not know the details of his journey but he seems to have started in the wilds of Lochaber. He then made surveys around John o' Groats and along the coasts of Cromarty, Inverness-shire and Morayshire before returning *via* Edinburgh where he spent a week's rest mainly with three professors at the university.

The government was so pleased with his report that he was asked to make a second survey in 1802. This time, he was also to enquire into emigration. He found that 3,000 Highlanders had left in 1801 and that three times as many expected to leave in 1802. The cause was lack of work, due partly to the switch to sheep, which were more profitable but needed less labour, and partly because poor communications made it almost impossible to develop other industries.

Telford's reports brought him great kudos; he was made a Fellow of the Royal Society of Edinburgh. They also brought him work. Parliament set up two Commissions to put his proposals into effect and appointed him engineer to both. He could thus oversee personally the whole of the master plan he had proposed. The cost of each individual scheme was divided equally between the government and local authorities and landowners.

Roads, bridges, and harbours

Over the next eighteen years, Telford was responsible for planning, designing, and building 1,200 bridges and 920 miles of new road in the Highlands. He also refurbished 280 miles of military roads. First priority was given to the bridges needed to eliminate

Telford's bridge over the River Spey at Craigellachie—one of the many bridges that eased communication and travel in the Highlands of Scotland.

the dangerous and time-wasting ferries. A bridge over the Tay at Dunkeld opened the way to the central Highlands. Bridges over the Beauly and Conon, together with some road improvements, eased the journey from Inverness to Dingwall. Other major bridges were built at Ballater and Potarch over the Dee, at Craigellachie over the Spey and at Bonar over the Dornoch Firth.

Meanwhile, Telford was pushing ahead with his new roads. In the west, he concentrated on improving access to the coast and thus to the islands. He started with a road from Fort William to Arisaig and another from Loch Oich, in the Great Glen, to Glen Garry and Loch Hourn. His road from Loch Ness through Glens Morriston and Shiel ran to the north of the first two and ended at the Kyle of Lochalsh. A short ferry connected with a road that ran the entire length of Skye.

Dingwall was the starting point of two other new roads, one running to Loch Carron on the west coast, with a branch to Loch Torridon, the other northwards to Bonar. The Bonar road continued across the middle of Sutherland to Tongue on the

Telford's first Scottish bridge was this one, crossing the River Dee at Tongueland, built in 1805–6. Unlike most of Telford's bridges, it is flat. Many of the others were rounded to let rainwater run off the roadway easily.

north coast. A branch swung eastwards along the Dornoch Firth and ran up the east coast to Wick and Thurso.

These were Telford's major Highland roads. They were fed by a network of smaller roads. He was also responsible for 184 miles of new road in the Lowlands, principally the main road from Carlisle to Glasgow with a cross route through Lanarkshire.

His method of road-making varied. In the Highlands, he used a technique that went back to the Romans. After levelling and draining, he made a pavement of large stones with their round or broad ends down. The points were broken off and the whole covered with a layer of stones the size of walnuts. Where possible, a thin layer of gravel was laid on top. Such a road bound quickly and lasted well.

The Lowland roads had to take much heavier traffic. He made them as level as possible and kept gradients down to one in thirty. This was especially important in the days when vehicles were drawn by horses. To strengthen the centre of the road, which was likely to take the greatest weight, he built with a

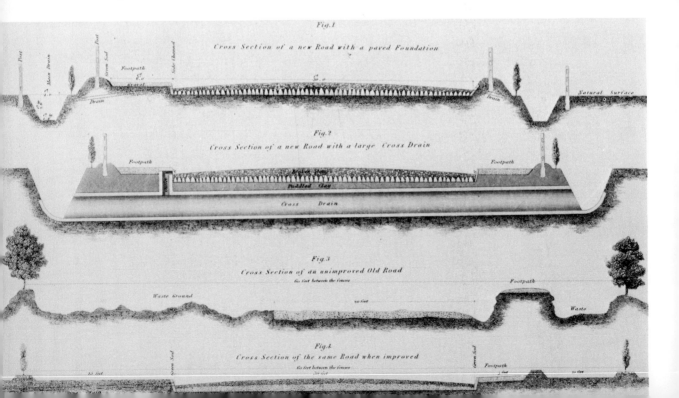

Fig. 1
Cross Section of a new Road with a paved Foundation

Fig. 2
Cross Section of a new Road with a large Cross Drain

Fig. 3
Cross Section of an unimproved Old Road

Fig. 4
Cross Section of the same Road when improved

camber of four inches. The under-paving was hand set with large stones, round end down. They were interbonded or jointed. This layer was seven inches deep but no stone was wider than three inches at the top. The gaps were filled in with smaller stones, packed by hand, to form an even surface.

A second course of seven inches was then added. It consisted of stones weighing not more than six ounces and able to pass through a ring two and a half inches in diameter. An inch-thick binding of gravel was laid on top. These roads were firm and dry in all weathers and needed little repair.

Left Various cross-sectional figures from Telford's *Atlas* showing road construction and improvement.

Right An actual cross-section of Telford's London to Holyhead road.

1½" GRAVEL.

2" OF STONE PASSING 2½" RING.

4" OF STONE PASSING 2½" RING.

PITCHING 7" – 9" DEEP.

SUBSOIL.

Conditions in the Highlands were often appalling. The mountainous terrain was cold and wet for much of the year. Many of the sites were so remote that mortar-lime had to be brought up by pack-horses, sometimes for distances of twenty miles. Stone for bridges was shipped to the nearest quay. Until 1824, when caravans with sleeping and cooking facilities for up to eighteen men were provided, the gangs had to sleep out in canvas tents or crude turf huts.

Perhaps Telford's greatest achievement was the organization he built up. He divided the area into six districts—Argyll, Badenoch, Lochaber, Skye, Ross-shire, Caithness-and-Sutherland—and appointed a superintendent for each. John Simpson was responsible for much of the masonry on bridges and William Hazledine provided most of the ironwork. Hazledine's foreman, William Stuttle, supervised erection.

Telford's only mistake was to appoint John Duncombe as general superintendent to oversee the district superintendents. He had worked well on the Ellesmere Canal but he was less happy in the Highlands.

We now see a less attractive side of Telford's character. He had no sympathy with failures. Of Duncombe, he wrote in 1809, "He seems to be getting into his dotage. There is no getting him to finish things in time. I have for ten weeks past stopped his salary and shall pay him only by the mile for what he really does." A few months later, Duncombe was jailed—we do not know why—and died before being released. Telford was as stony-hearted as his roads. "I am quite vexed about the old fool," he said. "His dying will not be a matter for regret but in a jail at Inverness is shocking."

Duncombe's replacement was John Mitchell, an outstanding success. He had been a working mason, scarcely able to read and write, when Telford first found him. Nicknamed "Telford's Tartar," he was

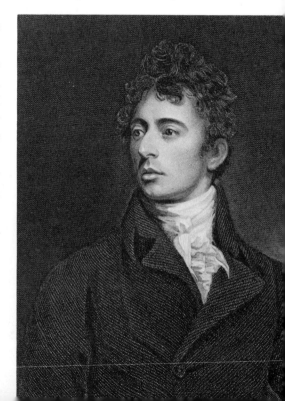

Robert Southey (1774–1843) poet laureate and friend of Telford, who went with him on one of his yearly tours of inspection in the Highlands.

immensely strong in both mind and body. He was a stickler for carrying out orders and landowners regularly complained of his toughness in negotiation. He drove himself equally hard, travelling up to 10,000 miles a year to inspect roads. After fourteen years he died. He had literally worked himself to death.

Telford kept a close eye on every stage of construction. As we shall see, he was busier than ever with other projects in England but he made at least one long visit to the Highlands each year. In 1819, one of his companions was the poet laureate Robert Southey. They were introduced by their mutual friend John Rickman, secretary to the two commissions.

Starting in Edinburgh, they travelled by Stirling, Callendar, and the Trossachs to Dunkeld and from there to Dundee and up the east coast to Stonehaven. From Aberdeen, they went on to Banff and Cullen, plunging inland to Fochabers, Craigellachie, and the Spey valley before returning to the coast at Nairn. They went on through Inverness and Dingwall to beyond the Dornoch Firth before crossing the Great

Dundee Harbour after Telford's improvements—one of a number of harbour improvements for which Telford was responsible.

Glen to Loch Eil. From there, they drove south to Dumbarton, finally parting at Longtown in Cumberland. Southey wrote of Telford, "A man more heartily to be liked, more worthy to be esteemed and admired, I have never fallen in with."

Their journey had lasted six weeks. During that time Telford had inspected not just roads and bridges but the various harbours on which he was working. We have not discussed these at length because it is not always clear how far the work was his own or based on the plans of other engineers such as John Smeaton or John Rennie. However, he was responsible for carrying out improvements in a number of harbours, including Aberdeen, Banff, Cullen, Dundee, Fraserburgh, Peterhead, and Kirkwall. He also built forty-two churches in the Highlands.

His work transformed the Highlands. The first stage-coaches ran from Perth to Inverness in 1806. Five years later, there was a regular service and by 1820, forty coaches a week were running in each direction. Carts replaced pack-horses. Fields could be manured more easily and imported building

Aberdeen Harbour after Telford's improvements.

materials made it possible to build substantial homes in place of mud cottages with a hole in the roof to let out smoke. Even dress improved as cheap clothes were brought in from Glasgow and Manchester.

Most important, Telford raised the general standard of workmanship out of all comparison. He wrote:

"About 3,200 men have been annually employed. At first, they could scarcely work at all: they were totally unacquainted with labour; they could not use the tools. They have since become excellent labourers, and of the above number we consider about one-fourth left us annually, taught to work. These undertakings may, indeed, be regarded in the light of a working academy, from which eight hundred men have annually gone forth improved workmen.

"They have either returned to their native districts with the advantage of having used the most perfect sort of tools and utensils (which alone cannot be estimated at less than ten per cent of any sort of labour), or they have been usefully distributed

Telford on a tour of inspection of road work in the Highlands in about 1820. With him is William Rickman, the son of Telford's friend John Rickman.

through the other parts of the country.

"Since these roads were made accessible, wheelwrights and cartwrights have been established, the plough has been introduced and improved tools and utensils are generally used. The moral habits of the great masses of the working classes are changed; they see that they may depend on their own exertions for support; this goes on silently, and is scarcely perceived until apparent by the results. I consider these improvements among the greatest blessings ever conferred on any country."

It is a large claim. But few would care to dispute it.

The Caledonian Canal

A major part of the master plan that Telford proposed for the Highlands was the building of a ship canal from the North Sea to the Atlantic through the Great Glen. The Caledonian Canal, as it came to be called, would be slightly more than sixty miles long. Since it would pass through some forty miles of navigable lochs, however, only about twenty miles had to be cut.

Even so, the twenty miles were through very difficult country. James Watt, the inventor of the steam engine, and John Rennie, the civil engineer, had both put forward schemes within the last thirty years but nothing had come of them.

The idea of a canal was attractive because of the high winds and stormy seas that made the Pentland Firth off the north-east tip of Scotland a death trap. Ships trading between Britain's eastern ports and America might be held up three months or more in winter. Those in favour of the canal told of two ships leaving Newcastle on the same day—one for Liverpool by the north of Scotland, the other for Bombay by the English Channel and the Cape of Good Hope. The ship sailing to Bombay arrived first. A canal

The Great Glen of Scotland, a rift valley cutting Scotland from Fort William to Inverness, through which Telford built the Caledonian Canal, seen here on the left of the River Lochy, looking north to Loch Lochy.

would also help the timber trade by shortening the journey between west coast ports and the Baltic.

Defence was another consideration. Britain was in the middle of the Napoleonic wars. An inland waterway would enable merchantmen to cross from one side of the country to the other without exposing themselves to French warships. Also, British warships stationed at Fort George near Inverness would be able to reach Northern Ireland in two days.

After touring the rugged country to the north of Lochs Lochy, Oich, and Ness, Telford consulted Watt

The Caledonian Canal was, as a feat of engineering, another triumph for Telford. As a vital waterway for trade or national defence it was a failure, dogged by bad luck and, in a number of places, slipshod workmanship.

and then returned to the Highlands with William Jessop. Further surveys and soundings were undertaken locally. The canal must be big enough to take a fully loaded 32-gun frigate. He therefore submitted plans for a channel that was 20 feet deep and tapered from a width of 110 feet at the surface to 50 feet at the bottom. It would take seven years to build. The estimated cost was £350,000. The government gave its approval and appointed Telford engineer.

His first job was to organize a labour force. He called his old friend Matthew Davidson from Shropshire, together with John Telford (no relation), and made them resident engineers. John Simpson was the contractor. The western end of the canal, for which John Telford was responsible, was extremely remote and houses had to be built for the masons. The labourers lived in barracks. Huge stocks of food were laid in and a brewery set up with the express intention of weaning the men from "the pernicious habit of drinking whisky." Two sloops, the *Corpach* and the *Caledonia*, were commissioned to ship in building materials.

The western basin of the canal was to be sited at Corpach at the head of Loch Eil. After fierce rows over the agreed wage of one shilling and sixpence a day, John Telford's men started work on the sea lock. They had to cut the chamber out of solid rock. It was kept free of water only by continuous pumping with a twenty-horsepower Boulton and Watt steam engine shipped from Birmingham. Two more locks carried it up to a level stretch of one mile. Then came eight more locks to raise the level to that of Loch Lochy which was ninety feet above sea level. These locks, at Banavie, were nicknamed Neptune's Staircase.

The poet Southey described the Staircase as having "more the effect of a scene in a pantomime than of anything in real life. The rise from lock to lock is eight feet—sixty-four, therefore in all. The length of the locks, including the gates and abutments at both ends is 500 yards—the greatest piece of such masonry in the world and the greatest work of the kind beyond all comparison." The only other major feature in the eight miles to Loch Lochy was a three-arch aqueduct over the River Loy.

Mountain streams poured down into the glen. Some were taken into the canal, others carried under it in culverts. In case the level of water became dangerously high, three outlet sluices were provided. Fully open, they could reduce the level of water along six miles of canal by one foot in an hour.

Telford opened them for Southey to see. "What would the Bourbons have given for such a cascade at Versailles?" he wrote. "The rush and the spray and the force of the water, reminded me more of the Reichenbach than of any other fall. That three small sluices, each only 4 feet by 3 feet, should produce an effect which brought the mightiest of the Swiss waterfalls to my recollection, may appear incredible . . ."

Meanwhile, Matthew Davidson had been pushing forward the eastern section from Clachnaharry near Inverness to Loch Ness. He was a bustling, opinionated Lowlander, rather like Dr. Johnson in appearance, and an avid reader. He was nicknamed "the Walking Library." He distrusted Highlanders. If the inhabitants of Inverness got their deserts, he said, the only people left after twenty years would be the provost and the hangman.

He faced an even more difficult problem than John Telford. The sea was so shallow that the entrance lock had to be built 400 yards offshore. The mud was at least 60 feet deep and so soft that nothing could be built on it. An artificial embankment was formed by dumping clay and stones in the sea. Only after allowing twelve months for it to settle could the masonry of the sea-lock be safely built. Here again, pumps were needed to keep the chamber free of water—one driven by horses, the other by a Boulton and Watt nine horsepower steam engine.

Map of Scotland showing roads, bridges, harbours, piers, canals and railways for which Telford was engineer.

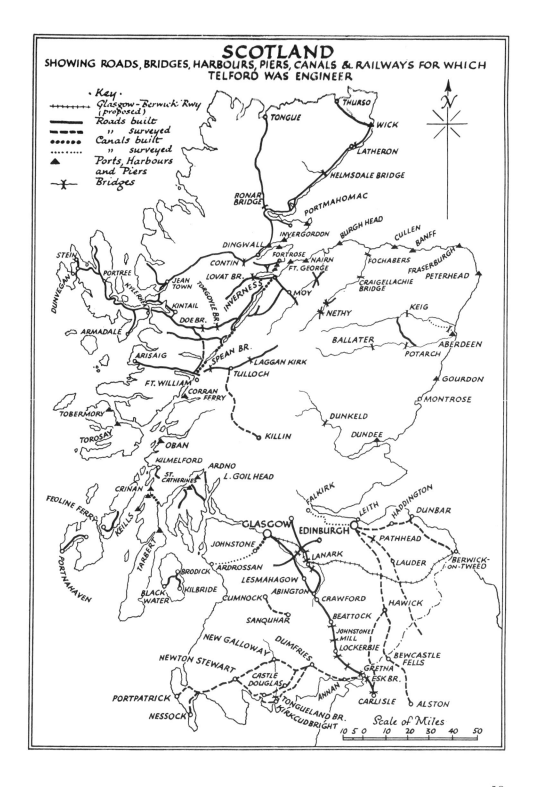

SCOTLAND

SHOWING ROADS, BRIDGES, HARBOURS, PIERS, CANALS & RAILWAYS FOR WHICH TELFORD WAS ENGINEER

· Key ·

‡‡‡‡‡ Glasgow – Berwick Rwy (proposed)
——— Roads built
– – – " surveyed
••••• Canals built
·········· " surveyed
▲ Ports, Harbours and Piers
⤬ Bridges

THURSO
TONGUE
WICK
LATHERON
HELMSDALE BRIDGE
RONAR BRIDGE
PORTMAHOMAC
BURGH HEAD
CULLEN
BANFF
INVERGORDON
DINGWALL
FORTROSE
NAIRN
FOCHABERS
FRASERBURGH
STEIN
CONTIN
FT. GEORGE
CRAIGELLACHIE BRIDGE
PETERHEAD
PORTREE
LOVAT BR.
JEAN TOWN
TORGOYLE BR.
INVERNESS
MOY
KYLERHE
KINTAIL
DOE BR.
NETHY
KEIG
ARMADALE
ABERDEEN
BALLATER
ARISAIG
SPEAN BR.
LAGGAN KIRK
POTARCH
FT. WILLIAM
TULLOCH
GOURDON
DUNVEGAN
CORRAN FERRY
MONTROSE
TOBERMORY
DUNKELD
TOROSAY
KILLIN
DUNDEE
OBAN
KILMELFORD
ARDNO
L. GOIL HEAD
FALKIRK
LEITH
HADDINGTON
CRINAN
ST. CATHERINES
GLASGOW
EDINBURGH
DUNBAR
FEOLINE FERRY
PATHHEAD
KEILLS
JOHNSTONE
LANARK
LAUDER
TARBERT
ARDROSSAN
LESMAHAGOW
BERWICK-ON-TWEED
PORTNAHAVEN
BRODICK
ABINGTON
CRAWFORD
HAWICK
BLACK WATER
KILBRIDE
CUMNOCK
BEATTOCK
SANQUHAR
JOHNSTONE MILL
NEW GALLOWAY
DUMFRIES
LOCKERBIE
BEWCASTLE FELLS
NEWTON STEWART
CASTLE DOUGLAS
GRETNA
ESK BR.
PORTPATRICK
ANNAN
CARLISLE
ALSTON
NESSOCK
TONGUELAND BR.
KIRKCUDBRIGHT

Scale of Miles
10 5 0   10   20   30   40   50

There were six more locks in the $7\frac{3}{4}$ miles between Clachnaharry and Loch Ness. Materials had to be brought from as far away as Nottingham and Wales, often in a third sloop, also called the *Caledonia*, assigned to the eastern section.

By 1820, the first two sections were almost finished and the labour forces moved up to work on the centre section. John Wilson, who succeeded John Telford on his death in 1807, was responsible for the stretch between Loch Lochy and Loch Oich. Matthew Davidson had also died, in 1818. His successor, John Cargill, took over the remaining section from Fort Augustus to Loch Oich. Two steam bucket dredgers were brought up from Nottingham to deepen the channel through Loch Oich and at the approaches to five more locks by Fort Augustus. They were also used on the Laggan cutting at the summit of the Canal. After digging part of the way down, the channel was flooded. It was then deepened by dredging.

The work was on a scale never before seen. The locks were 180 feet long. Men, horses, and machines toiled relentlessly. Up to ten vessels a day could now be seen on Loch Ness. They brought coal, food, and building materials directly to the site. The spoil was carried away by railways and barrow runs. But it was October, 1822 before the first ship sailed through the completed canal.

As a feat of engineering, the Caledonian Canal was another triumph for Telford. Yet it quickly turned sour. The final cost was almost £1,000,000. Instead of taking seven years to build, it took eighteen. The Napoleonic Wars had persuaded the government to approve the scheme. Britain had been at peace for more than seven years by the time it opened.

It was too small for many ships, partly because it had been impossible to dredge deeper than twelve feet through Loch Oich, partly because ships were now much larger than before. The age of steam had dawned. The new ships could slip easily through the

A Boulton and Watt pumping engine of the type used to keep the chamber of the sea-lock at Inverness free of water while it was being built.

61

Pentland Firth. Worse, a heavy government duty on Baltic timber to encourage the Canadian timber trade cost the Canal thousands of pounds in lost tolls.

The worst aspect was slipshod workmanship in the central section. One of the Fort Augustus locks blew out. Landslips blocked the Laggan cutting. By the 1830s, there was serious talk of closing the canal. The government decided to retain it and spent £200,000 on repairs and improvements. It was not fully open to traffic again until 1847.

One of Telford's successors as engineer to the Caledonian Canal summed up:

"The unfortunate issue of this great work was a grievous disappointment to Mr. Telford, and was in fact the one great bitter in his otherwise un-alloyed cup of happiness and prosperity. The un-dertaking was maligned by thousands who knew nothing of his character. It became 'a dog with a bad name,' and all the proverbial consequences followed. The most absurd errors and mis-conceptions were propagated respecting it from year to year, and it was impossible during Telford's lifetime to stem the torrent of popular prejudice and objurgation. It must, however, be admitted, after a long experience, that Telford was greatly over-sanguine in his expectations as to the national uses of the canal, and he was doomed to suffer acutely in his personal feelings, little though he may have been personally to blame, the consequences of what in this commercial country is regarded as so much worse than a crime, namely, a financial mis-take."

The Caledonian Canal by Loch Oich,
showing one of the locks.

5 London to Holyhead

At the beginning of the nineteenth century, Irish members of Parliament protested about the state of communications between Britain and Ireland. New landings at Howth near Dublin and Holyhead on Anglesey made possible a much shorter sea crossing than the previous one to Liverpool. This had often taken several days. But the road from London to Holyhead was still appalling.

Responsibility for keeping it in good repair was divided between twenty-four separate authorities. Those between Shrewsbury and Holyhead had little money to spend. The only transport between Shrewsbury and Bangor was a weekly cart, which ran in summer only. Travellers had to risk unfenced precipices, fords that quickly flooded and road sur-

Right Cast-iron details of the Waterloo Bridge at Bettwys-y-Coed. The rose, thistle, leek and shamrock, the emblems of England, Scotland, Wales and Ireland are sculpted beneath the curve of the arch and the inscription below them reads, "This arch was constructed in the same year as the battle of Waterloo was fought."

Below Telford's London to Holyhead road above Nant Ffrancon in North Wales.

faces so bad that the legs of three horses were broken in a single week.

In 1811, Telford was asked to survey a new route. He recommended a shortening of the road between Shrewsbury and Holyhead (109 miles) by some four miles. The new line via Llangollen, Corwen, Bettws-y-Coed, Capel Curig, and Bangor would have gradients not exceeding one in twenty. Those on the old road rose to one in six and a half. Four years later, a Board of Parliamentary Commissioners was appointed to take over the road. Telford became their engineer and the work began.

It took only four years to make the Welsh section safe and comfortable. Bends were straightened, hillsides blasted away. The old road climbed steeply into and out of deep valleys. Now, embankments were run out from the hillsides to join the bridge approaches, for instance over the chasm of the River Ogwen. The biggest embankment of all was built across the Stanley Sands between Anglesey and Holy Island. It was 1,300 yards long and 16 feet high, tapering from a width of 114 feet at the base to 34 feet at the top. A coating of rubble stone protected it against storms.

One of the most interesting features of the road is Waterloo Bridge at Bettws-y-Coed. Stone abutments support an elegant iron arch. In each of the two triangular spaces between the curve of the arch and the roadway overhead, rose, thistle, shamrock, and leek—the emblems of England, Scotland, Ireland, and Wales—are sculpted in iron. Underneath runs the legend, "This arch was constructed in the same year as the battle of Waterloo was fought." It shows a touch of originality so often missing from the soulless engineering jobs of our own time.

The old section of road from London to Shrewsbury was also far below standard. Steep hills made it exhausting for horses. Even on the outskirts of the capital, the surface often consisted of loose

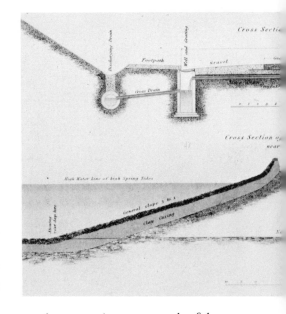

Road construction at two ends of the London to Holyhead road (from Telford's *Atlas*). Figure 5 shows a cross section of the Highgate Archway Road and Figure 6 shows a cross section of the Embankment at Stanley Sands near Holyhead.

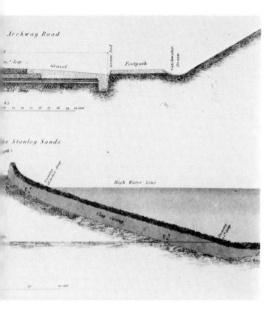

gravel sliding about on undrained clay. Banks of dirt blocked the highway between Towcester and Daventry. In winter, the mud was up to six inches deep.

Telford rebuilt the road and tidied up the route, making it easier, straighter, and flatter. He bypassed small villages. Typical improvements were the Highgate Archway cutting in London, the new London Road in St. Albans and reduced gradients at Hockcliffe, Meriden, Cosford, Ketley, and many other places.

His methods were expensive. They were also time-consuming. His improvements on the London–Holyhead road took fifteen years. But they were lasting and many are still in use. However, one link was still missing. The ferry across the narrow Menai Strait was both dangerous and unreliable, especially in winter. Some substitute must be found.

Between 1783 and 1810, Jessop, Rennie, and Telford himself were among the engineers who put forward schemes for a bridge. None was high enough to satisfy the Admiralty. The Strait must be open at all times to full-masted warships. The safety and convenience of travellers could not be allowed to interfere with Britain's defences.

In 1814, Telford was asked to advise on a bridge across the Mersey at Runcorn. The river was 1,200 feet wide and here too a high span was necessary so as not to obstruct shipping. The only solution was a suspension bridge. The principle had already been applied in India and America. The idea was to hang the road deck on rods suspended on chains strung between towers at each side. Telford made 200 tests to discover the most suitable kind of iron for the chains. He then designed a bridge with a centre span of 1,000 feet. Unfortunately, there was no money to build it.

Even so, the design was widely discussed. It prepared the Commissioners for Telford's proposal for a suspension bridge over the Menai Strait. He chose as his starting point Pig Island, a rock joined to the Anglesey shore by a causeway. The road deck of the bridge would span the channel at a height of 100 feet above the highest water at spring tides. Not even the tallest ship would ever be held up. The supporting piers would be 550 feet apart and would rise 53 feet above the level of the roadway. This would hang from sixteen main chains, whose links would consist of thirty-six bars of half-inch-square iron welded together.

The approach road from Anglesey would be carried on four arches, each of them with a span of 52 feet 6 inches. Three similar arches would support the road on the Caernarvonshire side. The road would have two carriageways, each twelve feet wide, with a four-foot path between them. The Commissioners approved the plan and work started in 1819.

A link bolt and coupling-plate used for the Menai Bridge.

The first job was to level off the rock surface at Pig Island by blasting. Rails were then run out from the shore. Horses dragged along them sledges loaded with stone shipped from the quarries at Penmon Point in the north-east corner of Anglesey. On 10th August, 1819, William Provis, the resident engineer, laid the first stone of the Pig Island pier. A base of solid rock for the pier on the Caernarvonshire side was found seven feet under the sand.

Meanwhile, workshops had been set up, five boats commissioned, a force of masons and labourers gathered together and quays built at Penmon Point and on both sides of the Strait for shipping stone. By June 1820, 300 men were at work. John Wilson, who had been one of Telford's most trusted helpers on the Caledonian Canal, was the masonry contractor. William Hazledine was responsible for the ironwork.

Telford took immense pains with the two main piers. They were built hollow with cross walls inside. To strengthen the suspension towers on top, iron dowels bound the individual stones together.

After some hundreds of experiments, the final form of the chains was decided on. Each link was nine feet long and was individually tested at Hazledine's works by one of Telford's own representatives. It had to be strong enough to carry a load of eleven tons per square inch of cross section. This was *double* the maximum load expected in practice but only *half* the load it could carry in theory. So the safety margin was huge.

Scale models showed the exact strength of the suspension rods that would be needed. Further tests across a nearby valley enabled Telford to work out the absolute weight of one of the main chains between the points of suspension. It was $23\frac{1}{2}$ tons. A strain of $39\frac{1}{2}$ tons would be needed to raise it into position.

The time had now come to raise the first chain. Unusually for him, Telford was anxious. He had slept badly for weeks. Despite the most careful planning, he could not be sure that the method he had worked out for tackling the next step would be successful.

The day chosen was 26th April, 1825. It was calm and bright. The Strait had been closed to shipping but dozens of pleasure craft gave sightseers a grandstand view. Thousands more gathered on each shore. At 2.30 p.m., an hour before high water, four boats towed out a raft and moored it between the piers. It was 450 feet long and 6 feet wide, and carried the central section of the chain. The Caernarvonshire end, firmly anchored in rock, hung down from the

69

The suspension bridge over the Menai
Straits—from Telford's *Atlas*.

Fig. 2
Manner of securing the ends of the Main Chains on the Anglesey side

Toll House

Natural Rock   Embankment of quarried Rock

Cast Iron Saddle

Natural Rock

Chamber for Main
Chain fastenings

N.B. Fig 1 represents
in the Plans Fig
are thrown into Pe

Fig. 4
Plan at the level of the Springing of the Stone Arches

Distance from Centre to Centre of Pyramids 579 feet 10½ inches
Span of the Catenary 570 feet . . . Versed Sine 43 feet
Height from Low Water Spring Tides to the Roadway 121 feet
. . . Dᵒ from High Water Spring Tides to . . . Dᵒ . . . 100 feet
Height of Main Suspending Pyramide above the Roadway 50 feet.

Carnarvonsh

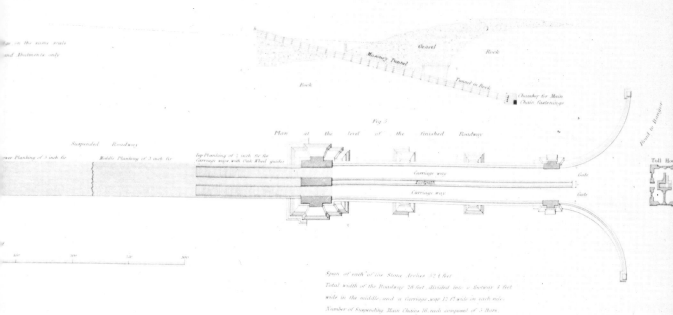

Fig 3
Manner of securing the ends of the Main Chains on the Carnarvonshire side

Gravel

Masonry Tunnel

Rock

Rock

Tunnel in Rock

*Chamber for Main
Chain Fastenings*

on the same scale

and Abutments only

Fig 5
Plan   at   the   level   of   the   finished   Roadway

Suspended   Roadway

lower Planking of 3 inch fir

Middle Planking of 3 inch fir

*Top Planking of 2 inch fir for
Carriage ways with Oak Wheel guides*

Carriage way

Gate

Carriage way

Gate

Road to Bangor

Toll House

Span of each of the Stone Arches 52 ½ feet

Total width of the Roadway 28 feet, divided into a footway 4 feet
wide in the middle, and a Carriage way 12 ½ wide on each side.

Number of Suspending Main Chains 16, each composed of 5 Bars,
and each Bar having a sectional area of 3 ¼ inches of Iron.

landward pier. One end of the central section was bolted to this. The other was joined to cables hanging down from the Pig Island pier. The Anglesey end of the chain reached only as far as the top of this pier.

On Anglesey itself, the cables ran to two capstans

A detail of the Menai Bridge showing its tension members, the massive links which form the "chain" by which the bridge is suspended.

manned by 150 labourers. The order "go along" rang out from the raft, a fife band struck up, and the men on the capstans chased round. As they hauled in the cables, the Anglesey end of the central section gradually rose towards the Pig Island pier.

One of the pulley blocks used on the Menai Bridge.

Then came the turn of the tide. When it was flowing strongly, the raft was cast off. This was the moment when Telford's calculations would be put to the test. If he had made a mistake, the cables would snap and the raft would end up at the bottom of the Strait. As the raft drifted downstream, the chain slid smoothly off. It hung safely in the air. A great cheer echoed across the water.

It took another hour and thirty-five minutes for it to be raised to the top of the Pig Island pier. Telford and Wilson had climbed up and watched while it was bolted to the Anglesey end. A second cheer went up, even greater than the first. Before anyone could stop them, three workmen scrambled on to the chain, which was only nine inches wide, and crawled like flies across the Strait to the pier on the Caernarvonshire side.

On 9th July, 1825, the final chain was hauled into place. A band climbed down to a platform built across the chains where they dipped to their lowest point more than a hundred feet above the water. The workmen marched across a temporary platform laid underneath and the *St. David* steam packet sailed through to celebrate the reopening of the Strait to navigation. The ever-present crowds cheered once again and the band played the National Anthem.

By our standards, it seems an extravagant way of celebrating. After all, the bridge would not be open for traffic until another six months had been spent laying the roadway, fixing side rails, and building toll-houses and approach roads. Yet at the time, it was the biggest bridge of its kind ever built. Some 33,265 pieces of iron weighing a total 2,187 tons had been used to produce a structure which one contemporary described as "more like the work of some magician than the mere result of man's skill and industry."

On 3rd April, 1822, contractors laid the first stone of a second suspension bridge at Conway. The main piers were cylindrical and topped with battlements to

The Menai Bridge today—a view across to Anglesey from Caernarvonshire.

harmonize with the towers of Conway Castle. The space between them was 327 feet. The eastern side was approached by an embankment 2,015 feet long and 300 feet wide at its highest part. It was finished less than six months after the Menai Bridge. The new route between London and Holyhead was now virtually complete.

Conway Bridge begun in 1822 and finished July 1826. Notice how the design of the bridge was made to blend in with Conway Castle behind it.

6 The Father of Civil Engineering

Any short biography of Telford is liable to become a mere catalogue of his work. The longer he lived, the more he became identified with it. He could rarely resist an invitation to add yet another job to a load that would have killed anyone else. Why did he do it?

Not for mere gain. He did not despise money but he was not obsessed with it either. His fees were small. He drew only £237 a year for the twenty-one years he acted as principal engineer to the Caledonian Canal. He did much public work completely free, for instance as engineer to the British Fisheries Society. He was scrupulous in never accepting gifts from contractors. At his death, it was found that he had never even bothered to count his money. He had nearly twice as much as he thought he had.

He lived on £1,200 a year, a modest sum for a man of his eminence. He kept a carriage but no horses. He always carried needle, thread, and buttons. After a full day's work, he would settle down at nine or nine-thirty in the evening to darn his own socks.

He was no longer a frugal eater. He enjoyed wine and good food. He was cheerful in any company, especially in that of children and young people. He had a dry wit. When a young man grossly overpraised an acquaintance's achievements, Telford asked, "Pray, can your friend lay eggs?" He had an unending fund of anecdotes.

Even so, he rarely went out in society. He had a few close personal friends such as Southey and later, the Scottish poet Thomas Campbell. He still spent most of his leisure reading in French, German, or English. He also wrote—for instance, articles on Architecture, Bridge-building and Canal-making for the Edinburgh Encyclopaedia.

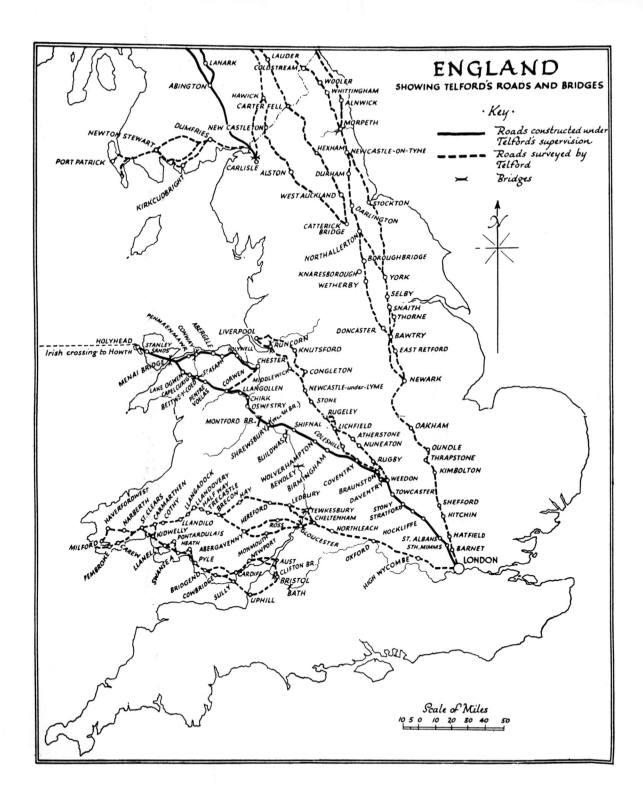

ENGLAND
SHOWING TELFORD'S ROADS AND BRIDGES

· Key ·

——— Roads constructed under Telford's supervision

- - - - Roads surveyed by Telford

—⟩— Bridges

LANARK
LAUDER
COLDSTREAM
ABINGTON
WOOLER
HAWICK
WHITTINGHAM
CARTER FELL
ALNWICK
NEW CASTLETON
MORPETH
NEWTON STEWART
DUMFRIES
HEXHAM
NEWCASTLE-ON-TYNE
PORT PATRICK
CARLISLE
ALSTON
DURHAM
KIRKCUDBRIGHT
WEST AUCKLAND
STOCKTON
DARLINGTON
CATTERICK BRIDGE
NORTHALLERTON
BOROUGHBRIDGE
KNARESBOROUGH
YORK
WETHERBY
SELBY
SNAITH
THORNE
HOLYHEAD
PENMAEN MAWR
CONWAY
ABERGELE
LIVERPOOL
DONCASTER
BAWTRY
Irish crossing to Howth
STANLEY SANDS
HOLYWELL
RUNCORN
MENAI BRIDGE
KNUTSFORD
EAST RETFORD
LAKE OGWEN
ST ASAPH
CHESTER
CAPEL CURIG
CORWEN
CONGLETON
NEWARK
BETTWS-Y-COED
MIDDLEWICH
DENTRE VOELAS
LLANGOLLEN
NEWCASTLE-under-LYME
CHIRK
OSWESTRY
STONE
MONTFORD BR.
(WELSH BR.)
RUGELEY
SHIFNAL
LICHFIELD
OAKHAM
SHREWSBURY
COLESHILL
ATHERSTONE
BUILDWAS
NUNEATON
HAVERFORDWEST
WOLVERHAMPTON
OUNDLE
WELSHPOOL
BEWDLEY
BIRMINGHAM
RUGBY
THRAPSTONE
LLANGADOCK
COVENTRY
WEEDON
KIMBOLTON
NARBERTH
LLANDOVERY
HALF WAY
BRAUNSTON
ST CLEARS
TRECASTLE
HAY
LEDBURY
DAVENTRY
TOWCESTER
CARMARTHEN
COTHY
BRECON
HEREFORD
STONY
SHEFFORD
CHELTENHAM
STRATFORD
MILFORD
LLANDILO
ROSS
TEWKESBURY
HITCHIN
KIDWELLY
PONTARDULAIS
NORTHLEACH
HOCKLIFFE
HATFIELD
CAREW
NEATH
ABERGAVENNY
GLOUCESTER
ST. ALBANS
PEMBROKE
MONMOUTH
OXFORD
STH. MIMMS
BARNET
LLANELL
PYLE
NEWPORT
LONDON
SWANSEA
AUST
HIGH WYCOMBE
BRIDGEND
CARDIFF
CLIFTON BR.
COWBRIDGE
SULLY
BRISTOL
UPHILL
BATH

Scale of Miles
10 5 0 10 20 30 40 50

The rest of his life was work. He relished every minute. In London, he entertained colleagues and business contacts. In the provinces, he was to be found presiding over dinners with his navvies in public houses. He continually surprised them with his memory for details of their lives and their families.

He was known at inns the length and breadth of Great Britain. He spent months at a time on the road. In his book *Thomas Telford,* L. T. C. Rolt quotes from a letter written from Glasgow in October 1816. Telford was then almost sixty.

"After Parliament was prorogued, I went thro' North Wales where about 500 men are employed, & from thence into and along all the Eastern side of Ireland from Waterford to Belfast & Donaghadee and across by Portpatrick to Carlisle, from thence to Glasgow and back by Moffat to Edinburgh. From thence by St. Andrews & Dundee to Aberdeen, then up the Western parts of that County, then across it and Banffshire and to every Town on that Coast to Inverness—thence thro' Ross and Sutherland & back to Inverness—from thence across to Fort William on the West Sea and back to Inverness—then back to Fort William. From thence by Tyndrum & Inverary down to the Crinan Canal in Cantyre, thence back by Inverary and Loch Lomond to Glasgow and again still nearly the same route and back to Inverness and west by the Crinan Canal and Glasgow to perform over again before I reach the Border."

He spent another month surveying the route of the Glasgow–Carlisle road in heavy snow before driving back to London.

Any one of a dozen schemes for which he was responsible would have been the high point of a lesser man's career—a six-year survey of the Great North Road, a survey of a Bristol–Milford Haven route to link with the new Irish ferry, three major bridges over

Map of England showing Telford's roads and bridges.

The Dean Bridge over the Water of Leith, Edinburgh, one of the two last and greatest of the stone bridges built by Telford.

The St. Katherine's Dock in London, built by Telford, beginning in 1826. The project involved demolishing 1,250 houses and the old St. Katherine's Hospital, and was completed with extraordinary speed in only two and a half years.

the Severn at Tewkesbury, Gloucester, and Holt Fleet, the Dean Bridge over the Water of Leith at Edinburgh, the Broomielaw Bridge in Glasgow.

He built the St. Katharine's dock in London, drained the North Level of the Fens and, as engineering adviser to the Exchequer Loan Commission which lent money for new works, reported on the Bude Canal, the Gloucester and Berkeley Canal, and several others. He built the Gotha Canal across Sweden and was consulted on roads and bridges by the Austrian and Russian governments. In 1825, he was asked about the cutting of a canal across the Isthmus of Darien, now Panama.

He often visited London on business and for twenty-one years stayed at the Salopian Coffee House (really an hotel) at Charing Cross. The Salopian became a recognized meeting place for engineers

both British and foreign. Eventually, he had his own suite of rooms where he conducted much of his business. When the coffee house was sold to a new landlord, the price was raised to take account of the trade he attracted. One buyer found a premium of £450 good value. His successor was less fortunate. Soon after he took over, Telford announced that he was leaving. "What! Leave!" he exclaimed. "Sir, I have just paid £750 for you."

Telford moved to 24, Abingdon Street, a house once occupied by Sir William Chambers who had been his first London employer. He delighted in showing visitors the solid mahogany doors and marble fireplaces. Part of the house was given over to his assistants and pupils.

For some years, leading engineers had been meeting once a fortnight at an inn in Holborn, later at the Crown and Anchor in the Strand. After dining together, they spent the evening discussing engineering topics. As the profession grew in both size and importance, half a dozen younger members decided that a more formal organization was needed. They drew up a constitution but after two years succeeded in attracting only four new members. However, one of them was William Provis, who had worked on the Menai Bridge. Telford was now generally acknowledged as the head of his profession and Provis suggested that they approach him for his support. On 21st March, 1820, Telford became the first President of the Institution of Civil Engineers.

Every Tuesday, he held a dinner for engineering friends at Abingdon Street. Afterwards, they went along to the weekly meeting of the Institution which was held in a house in Buckingham Street off the Strand. At first, there were rarely more than thirty present but through Telford's influence, numbers gradually built up. He supplied it with the nucleus of a reference library and in 1828 was instrumental in obtaining for it a charter of incorporation.

The Gotha Canal as it is today. It was designed by Telford, begun in 1809 and finally completed in 1832 giving Sweden a waterway from the Baltic to the North Sea.

By now, he was seventy-one. He was growing deaf and his energy was at last failing him. We know very little of his personal life or outlook during these last years but he continued to keep in touch with his Langholm friends and made a point of sending between £30 and £50 each year to be given to the poor.

He started work on his autobiography. Looking back over his life, he still thought that his training as a mason was the best start he could have had. He advised a friend seeking advice on how a young man should embark on a career in civil engineering:

Isambard Kingdom Brunel (1806–1859), whose design for a bridge over the Avon Gorge at Bristol was accepted in preference to Telford's.

"The way in which both Mr. Rennie and myself proceeded was to serve a regular apprenticeship to some practical employment—he to a millwright, I to a general house-builder. In this way, we secured the means, by hard labour, of earning a subsistence; and in time, we obtained by good conduct the confidence of our employers and the public; eventually rising into the rank of what is called Civil Engineering. This is the true way of acquiring practical skill, a thorough knowledge of the materials employed in construction, and last, but not least, a perfect knowledge of the habits and dispositions of the workmen who carry out our designs."

Professionally, he himself was now losing ground. Invited to judge a competition for a bridge over the Avon Gorge at Bristol he turned down a design for a suspension bridge submitted by an upstart of twenty-four called Isambard Kingdom Brunel. The proposed span of 916 feet was, he said, too long for safety. He himself designed an alternative with two huge piers set in the floor of the Gorge carrying a much shorter span. Brunel scoffed. The decision was put to the committee responsible for the bridge. They chose Brunel's design, not Telford's.

The opening of the Stockton and Darlington Railway in 1825 was another sign that time was passing him by. He approved of railways where steep hills or lack of water made canals impossible. Otherwise, he disliked their rigidity. He thought that steam locomotives could best be used on ordinary roads.

As engineer to the Exchequer Loan Commission, he was obliged to report on railways that applied for aid but wherever possible he remained loyal to the canal companies which had given him his chance in life. They were now seriously threatened. Long delayed repairs and improvements were hurriedly put in hand. Although he wanted to cut down on his work, he agreed to build the new Harecastle tunnel on the Trent and Mersey Canal. He surveyed the line of the Macclesfield Canal. He built a new cutting for the Birmingham Canal at Smethwick.

His last major work was the Birmingham and Liverpool Junction Canal, started in 1826 and scheduled for completion in 1830. The aim was to forestall the proposed Birmingham and Liverpool Railway by cutting a waterway from the Staffordshire and Worcestershire Canal near Wolverhampton to Nantwich on the Ellesmere and Chester. It would provide a through route from the Midlands to the Mersey.

It was no easy task. The route, some of it through difficult country, was made even more awkward by landowners who refused to allow the new canal through their parks. To carry it round one jealously

The opening of the Stockton and Darlington Railway in 1825, heralding the new age of the railway—just one of the signs that time was beginning to pass Telford by.

guarded wood, the contractors had to build the Shelmore embankment, an earthwork sixty feet high. Work began on it in 1829. Massive subsidences brought repeated delays. Telford was now ailing. He handed over to William Cubitt. Shelmore Bank was completed six years after starting, making the opening of the canal five years late. By that time, Telford had been dead six months.

He had finally given in to repeated bouts of sickness on 2nd September, 1834, at the age of seventy-seven. Although he had asked to be buried at the parish church of St. Margaret's, Westminster, members of the Institution of Civil Engineers insisted that Westminster Abbey would be more appropriate. His remains lie under a stone inscribed "Thomas Telford, 1834" near the middle of the nave.

Believing he had only £16,000 to bequeath, he left

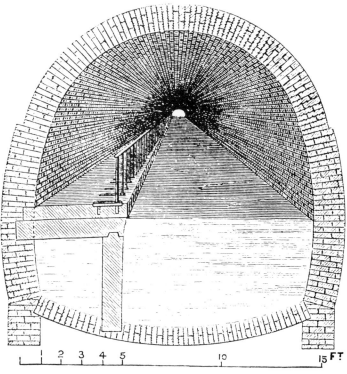

Above Cross-section of Telford's part of the Harecastle Tunnel on the Grand Junction Canal.

£2,000 to the Institution of Civil Engineers and £1,000 each to the parish libraries of Langholm and Westerkirk. The rest went in sums of between £200 and £500 to employees, colleagues, and friends, including Southey and Campbell. As his estate was found to total some £30,000, the bequests were increased accordingly.

Yet his greatest bequest was to his own profession. Without his support, it is unlikely that the Institution of Civil Engineers would have survived. It might have been many years before others founded a body of equivalent standing. He was above all the Father of Civil Engineering.

The northern entrance to the Harecastle Tunnel on the Grand Trunk Canal. The entrance on the right is Brindley's and that on the left of it is Telford's. This was one of Telford's last major jobs and was completed in 1826.

Date Chart

1757	Born 9th August at Glendinning near Langholm, Dumfriesshire.
1757	Father, John Telford, dies in November.
1760	Accession of King George III.
1761–5	Bridgewater Canal from Worsley to Manchester built by James Brindley.
1769	James Watt patents his steam engine.
1771	Telford leaves school. Apprenticed as a mason.
1780	Works in Edinburgh as a mason. Studies architecture.
1782	Rides to London. Works as mason at Somerset House.
1784–6	Supervises the building of a house for the Commissioner of Portsmouth Dockyard. Joins the Freemasons.
1787	Sir William Pulteney hires him to supervise alterations to Shrewsbury Castle.
1787–93	New prison at Shrewsbury.
1788	County Surveyor of Shropshire.
1792	Study tour of Gloucester, Worcester, Bath, London, and Oxford.
1793	General agent of the Ellesmere Canal. French Wars begin.
1795	Wirral section of Ellesmere Canal opened. Work starts on Pont Cysyllte aqueduct.
1795–1800	Engineer to Shrewsbury Canal.
1796	Engineer to British Fisheries Society.
1796–1834	Work on a great many harbours in England, Scotland, Wales, and Ireland.
1801	First Highland survey.
1802	Second Highland survey. Fellow of the Royal Society of Edinburgh.

1803	Work starts on the Caledonian Canal.
1803–20	920 miles of roads built in the Highlands. Also, 1,200 bridges.
1805	Pont Cysyllte aqueduct completed. Ellesmere Canal open to Mersey.
1806	Isambard Kingdom Brunel born at Portsmouth. Telford becomes engineer to Glasgow Waterworks.
1808	Survey of the Gotha Canal across Sweden.
1809–33	Building of Gotha Canal.
1810	Survey of roads in North Wales.
1814–25	Carlisle to Glasgow road.
1815	Plan for suspension bridge across Menai Strait. Battle of Waterloo. End of French Wars.
1815–29	Shrewsbury to Bangor road improvements.
1817	Adviser on engineering to the Exchequer Loan Commission.
1818–34	Engaged in several schemes for draining the Fens, especially the North Level.
1819	Tour of Scotland with the poet Robert Southey.
1820	First President of the Institution of Civil Engineers. Accession of George IV.
1820–26	Surveys of the Great North Road.
1820–28	London to Shrewsbury road improvements.
1821	Conway bridge started.
1822	The first ship sails through the Caledonian Canal.
1822–27	Harecastle Tunnel on the Trent and Mersey Canal.
1824–34	Forty-two Highland churches built. Reconstruction of the Birmingham Canal.
1825	Reported on plan for a Panama Canal. Advised Russian government on War-

	saw–Briesc road. Stockton–Darlington Railway opened.
1825–34	Birmingham and Liverpool Junction Canal.
1826	Menai and Conway Bridges completed. London–Holyhead road fully open. St Katharine's Dock, London.
1827	Fellow of the Royal Society.
1829	Report to the Exchequer Loan Commission on the Liverpool and Manchester Railway.
1829–30	Brunel's plan for a Clifton Gorge suspension bridge in Bristol preferred to Telford's.
1829–31	Dean Bridge over the water of Leith, Edinburgh.
1829–36	Broomielaw Bridge over the Clyde, Glasgow.
1830	Accession of William IV.
1834	Death of Telford on 2nd September. Buried in Westminster Abbey.

Glossary

AQUEDUCT   Bridge carrying waterway, e.g. over a road or river.

ASHLAR   Built with square hewn stones.

BATTLEMENT   Parapet with tooth-like notches.

CAMBER   Arching of a road surface from side to side.

CAPSTAN   Revolving post, worked by men pushing against horizontal arms, to wind in a cable, anchor, etc.

CARTWRIGHT   A maker of carts.

CAS-CHROM   Primitive "plough" used in the Highlands until the early nineteenth century. It was pushed by hand.

CONCESSIONAIRE   Holder of a right to use something, often for profit, usually a monopoly.

CONTRACTOR   One who undertakes to do a piece of work.

DREDGE   To scoop up mud, stones and so on from the bottom of a lake, river, canal, or sea.

FLANGE   An edge projecting from a wheel or plate.

GRADIENT   Degree of slope in a road or railway.

GRAVING DOCK   A dry dock where ships' bottoms can be cleaned.

LOCK   Section of canal, cut off by sluiced gates, where boats can be raised or lowered to a different level.

MASON   A worker in stone.

MASON'S MARK   Device carved on stone by a mason to identify his work.

NAVVY   Labourer employed on the building of a road, canal, or railway.

PARKER'S CEMENT   Early form of waterproof cement.

PIER   Pillar supporting a bridge.

PUDDLE   Damp clay used as watertight lining for

aqueducts, embankments and so on.

SLUICE   Device for controlling the level of water by releasing it—for instance, through a sliding gate.

SOUNDING   A test of depth.

SUSPENSION BRIDGE   A bridge whose deck is hung from chains slung between towers.

TOLL-HOUSE   Place where tolls, or fees, are collected.

WEIR   A dam to raise the level of water in a river or lake.

WHEELWRIGHT   A maker of wheels.

Further Reading

Easily the best account of Telford's life and work is *Thomas Telford* by L. T. C. Rolt (Longmans, London, 1958).

Other books worth looking at are:

Gibb, Sir Alexander, *The Story of Telford*. (Maclehose, London, 1935).

Hadfield, E. C. R., *British Canals*. (Phoenix House, London, 1950).

Haldane, A. R. B., *New Ways Through the Glens*. (David and Charles, Newton Abbot, 1973).

Smiles, Samuel, *The Life of Thomas Telford*. (Murray, London, 1867).

Southey, Robert, *Journal of a Tour in Scotland in 1819*. (Murray, London, 1929).

Telford, Thomas, *Life of Thomas Telford*. ed. John Rickman. (Hansard, London, 1838).

Index

Numbers in italics refer to illustrations or captions

Picture Credits

The author and publishers wish to thank all those who have given their kind permission for illustrations to appear on the following pages: Aerofilms, 55, 56, 63; Eric de Maré, 29, 35, 40, 47, 65, 72, 75, 80, 82–83, 84; The Mansell Collection, *frontispiece*, 26, 30–31, 33, 43; Mary Evans Picture Library, 11, 19, 20, 21, 22, 23, 30, 50, 81; Ronan Picture Library, jacket picture, 13, 15, 26, 28, 36–37, 44–45, 46, 51, 52, 64, 87, 88; Royal Commission on Historical Monuments (England), 76; Science Museum, 8, 42, 48, 49, 60–61, 66–67, 68, 70–71, 73, 86–87. The remaining pictures are from the Wayland Picture Library.

DATE DUE

MY 23 '86			
GAYLORD			PRINTED IN U.S.A.